Funny Jokes

This edition published in 2020 by Arcturus Publishing Limited
26/27 Bickels Yard, 151–153 Bermondsey Street,
London SE1 3HA

Copyright © Arcturus Holdings Limited

All rights reserved. No part of this publication may be reproduced,
stored in a retrieval system, or transmitted, in any form or by any means,
electronic, mechanical, photocopying, recording or otherwise, without
prior written permission in accordance with the provisions of the
Copyright Act 1956 (as amended). Any person or persons who do any
unauthorised act in relation to this publication may be liable to criminal
prosecution and civil claims for damages.

Cover artwork: Adam Clay
All other illustrations: Shutterstock
Editor: Donna Gregory
Designer: Steve Flight

CH007421NT
Supplier 40, Date 0620, Print run 9411

Printed in the UK

What do you call a wizard who's really good at golf?

Harry Putter.

Why did the spaceship land outside my bedroom?

You must have left the landing light on!

What do you call a bad-tempered bee?

A grumblebee.

Why are dogs such bad dancers?

They have two left feet.

What do you get if you cross a vampire with a circus entertainer?

Someone who goes straight for the juggler!

What is a polygon?

A dead parrot.

What kind of key opens a banana?

A monkey!

What's worse than raining cats and dogs?

Hailing taxis.

Who built the Ark?

I have Noah idea.

Where were the traitors beheaded?

Just above the shoulders!

Did you hear about the cannibal who was expelled from school?

He was buttering up the teachers.

HA!

HA! HA HA HA! HA HA HA HA HA! HA I HA!

What happened to the cat that swallowed a ball of wool?

She had mittens.

What do you get if you cross a vampire with a mummy?

Something you wouldn't want to unwrap!

Why do roosters curse all the time?

They are fowl-mouthed.

What sort of dancing will elephants do in your front room?

Break dancing!

What do ghosts eat for dinner?

Ghoulash!

What did the waiter say when the horse walked into the café?

Why the long face?

How do hippos commute?

By hippopotabus.

HA HA HA

How can you keep a wet dog from smelling?

Hold its nose.

What do you call the Roman Emperor who kept pet mice?

Julius Cheeser!

LOL

Teacher: What language do they speak in Cuba?

Pupil: Cubic!

How did Moses cut the sea in half?

With a sea-saw.

Have you put some more water in the goldfish bowl?

No. It still hasn't drunk the water I put in when I first bought it!

Why did one pencil tell the other pencil it looked old and tired?

Because it was blunt.

Why can't I get the king of the jungle on the telephone?

Because the lion is busy!

Why didn't the skeleton fight the monster?

He didn't have the guts!

What did the chicken say when it laid a square egg?

Owwww!

What do you call a lion with toothache?

Rory!

How do ghosts begin business letters?

Tomb it may concern...

What did the flamenco-dancing farmer say to his chickens?

Oh, lay!

What's the tastiest class at school?

History. It's full of dates.

Teacher: Why did Robin Hood steal from the rich?

Pupil: Because the poor didn't have anything worth stealing!

Hey, you can't fish here, this is a private lake!

I'm not fishing, I'm teaching my pet worm to swim!

How do fleas get from one animal to another?

They itch hike!

My music teacher said I have a heavenly voice!

That's not strictly true; she said your voice was like nothing on Earth!

Two wrongs don't make a right, but what do two rights make?

The first plane!

Why did the rubber chicken cross the road?

She wanted to stretch her legs.

What happened to the vampire with bad breath?

His dentist told him to gargoyle twice a day!

Teacher: Have you written your essay on big cats?

Pupil: I thought it would be safer to use paper!

What has a pointy hat, a broomstick, and a blue face?

A witch holding her breath.

First Roman soldier: What's the time?

Second Roman soldier: XV past VIII.

First Roman soldier: By the time I work that out, it will be midnight!

What do you call a hippo that always claims to be sick?

A hippochondriac.

What do you get if you feed gunpowder to a chicken?

An egg-splosion!

What's the special offer at the pet store this week?

Buy one cat, get one flea!

Teacher: You missed school yesterday, didn't you?

Pupil: Not very much!

What is an archeologist?

Someone whose career is in ruins.

HA HA HA

What sum do teachers like best?

The summer.

What do you call a multi-level pigpen?

A styscraper.

How can you tell when there's a giant monster under your bed?

When your nose touches the ceiling.

Why is cutting a slice of gingerbread the easiest job in the world?

It's a piece of cake.

Why did the firefly keep crashing?

He wasn't very bright.

Why did the dog wear gloves?

Because it was a boxer.

Teacher: How did the Dark Ages get their name?

Pupil: Because there were so many knights!

What did King Kong say when he was told that his sister had had a baby?

Well, I'll be a monkey's uncle!

Where do horses stay in hotels?

The bridle suite.

Teacher: Why are you taking that sponge into class?

Pupil: Because I find your classes so absorbing!

What do vampires do at eleven o'clock every night?

They have a coffin break.

What do you call the king who invented the fireplace?

Alfred the Grate!

Why was the mathematics textbook miserable?

It had too many problems.

How does Frankenstein's monster sit in a chair?

Bolt upright!

What do you call a show full of lions?

The mane event.

My dog's a blacksmith.

How can you tell?

When I tell him off, he makes a bolt for the door.

What did the farmer use to paint the new sty?

Pigment.

What did King Henry VIII do whenever he burped?

He issued a royal pardon.

Why was the music teacher locked out of his classroom?

The keys were on the piano.

Why was the cat scared of the tree?

Because of its bark.

What was written on the robot's gravestone?

Rust in pieces!

Why did the monkey like the banana?

Because it had appeal!

Who is in charge of the stick insects?

The branch manager!

Where was the Declaration of Independence signed?

At the bottom.

How do you know that smoking is harmful to your health?

Well, look what happened to all the dragons!

Baby snake: Dad, are we poisonous?

Dad snake: No, son, why do you ask?

Baby snake: I've just bitten my tongue!

What animal wears a long coat in the winter and pants in the summer?

A dog!

What do you call a factual TV show about sheep?

A flock-umentary!

English teacher: Give me an example of a long sentence.

Pupil: Life imprisonment.

How did Vikings send secret messages?

By Norse code.

Why did it take the Dalmatian so long to choose a vacation?

He was looking for just the right spot.

HA
HA
HA

What did the pencil say to the protractor?

Take me to your ruler.

Knock, knock!

Who's there?

Orange!

Orange who?

Orange you glad to see me?

Why did the goose cross the road?

To prove she wasn't chicken!

What is a monster's fave party game?

Swallow the leader!

I sprained my ankle and had to miss gym for two weeks.

Lucky you. Our gym teacher never accepts a lame excuse for his class!

Patient: Doctor, I got trampled by a load of cows!

Doctor: So I herd!

Should monsters eat people on an empty stomach?

No, they should eat them on a plate!

Which emperor should never have played with explosives?

Napoleon Blownapart!

Spotted in the jungle library:

Why Giant Snails Get Tired, by Michelle Sevy

What is a good pet for small children?

A rattlesnake!

What type of dog can tell the time?

A watchdog.

Why do historians believe that Rome was built at night?

Because it wasn't built in a day.

What do you call an alligator private eye?

An investi-gator.

What do you give a pony with a cold?

Cough stirrup!

Why don't skeletons sing church music?

They have no organs.

Why don't leopards bother to cheat in exams?

Because they know they will always be spotted!

What goes WOO-HA-HA THUMP?

Frankenstein's monster laughing his head off.

Why should you never tell your secrets to a piglet?

Because they might squeal!

My English teacher is a real peach!

You mean she's pretty?

No. I mean she has a heart of stone!

What do you get if you cross a tarantula with a rose?

We're not sure, but don't try smelling it!

How do you spell mousetrap using only three letters?

C A T!

In which battle was Alexander the Great killed?

His last one!

Why don't bananas sunbathe?

Because they would peel.

Is the **mathematics teacher** in a good mood today?

I wouldn't count on it!

Which pets are the noisiest?

Trumpets!

What job does Dracula have with the Transylvanian baseball team?

He looks after the bats!

Teacher: Can you define the word hardship?

Silly pupil: Is it a boat made out of concrete?

What was King John's castle renowned for?

Its knight life.

Why do ghosts never feel guilty?

They have a clear conscience!

Where did Viking teachers send sick children?

To the school Norse.

What do history teachers do before they get married?

They go out on dates!

What did the dog say when it sat on some sharp stones?

Ruff!

What happens if you cross a hummingbird with a doorbell?

You get a humdinger.

HA HA HA

How do alien farmers round up their sheep?

They use tractor beams!

Teacher: Today we're studying ancient Rome. Can anyone tell me what a forum was?

Pupil: A two-um plus a two-um?

Classified ad in local paper:

Dog free to good home. Eats anything. Loves children!

What do you call a lion with no eyes?

Lon!

Why is 6 afraid of 7?

Because 7 ate 9!

First friend: Did you know that you can get fur from a vampire?

Second friend: Really? What kind of fur?

First friend: As fur away as possible!

What do you get when you cross a chicken and a fox?

Just the fox.

Parent: Why have you given my son such a bad mark? He's as intelligent as the next boy!

Teacher: Yes, but the next boy is an idiot!

Which historical character was always eating?

Attila the Hungry!

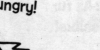

Why do vampires dislike computers?

They hate anything new-fang-led!

How can you cook turkey that really tickles the taste buds?

Leave the feathers on!

What does the lemur do every evening?

He curls up with his best-loved tail.

How do you stop a dog from barking in the back seat of a car?

Put it in the front seat.

Why did the dog limp into the Wild West saloon?

He came to find the cowboy who shot his paw!

How many pigs do you need to make a smell?

A phew!

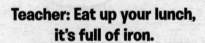

Teacher: Eat up your lunch, it's full of iron.

Pupil: That explains why it's so difficult to chew!

Why does a frog have more lives than a cat?

Because it croaks every night.

Why did the car stop when it saw the monster truck?

It had a nervous breakdown.

What did Robin Hood say when he was almost hit at the archery tournament?

That was an arrow escape!

What do you call a cow with an out-of-date map?

Udderly lost!

How did you know I was a ghost?

Oh, I can see right through you!

HA! HA
HA HA.
HA HA HA
! HA I HA
! HA!

What's orange and sounds like a parrot?

A carrot.

Parent: Do you think my son has what it takes to become a pilot?

Teacher: Well, he certainly spends plenty of time with his head in the clouds!

I think I'm turning into a young cat.

You're kitten me!

What did Attila's wife say to get his attention?

Over here, Hun.

Teacher: How did people spend their time in the Stone Age?

Pupil: Did they listen to rock music?

Why did King Arthur have a Round Table?

So that no one could corner him.

What do you call a cat that chases outlaws?

A posse cat!

Why was young Dr. Frankenstein so popular?

Because he was great at making new friends!

Where do cows go for history lessons?

To a mooseum!

How do you fix a broken chimp?

With a monkey wrench!

How did the ghostly teacher make sure his pupils had learned what he had written on the board?

He went through it again!

What happens when music teachers are sick?

They send in a note!

Which fairy tale do pigs like best?

Slopping Beauty.

What do you get if you cross an insect and a rabbit?

Bugs Bunny.

What did the caveman give his girlfriend on Valentine's Day?

Ugs and kisses.

Is it hard to spot a leopard?

Not at all, they come that way!

What do Alexander the Great and Billy the Kid have in common?

The same middle name.

Did you hear about the well-behaved cat?

It was purrfect.

What advice did the parrot give to the toucan?

Talk is cheep.

If a small duck is called a duckling, what do you call a small pen?

An inkling!

Did you hear about the mathematics teacher whose mistakes started to multiply?

In the end, they had to take him away!

How do vampires get clean?

In a blood bath!

Mother: You can't keep a pig in your bedroom, what about the terrible smell?

Child: Don't worry, he'll soon get used to it!

Why did the monster buy a hatchet?

Because he wanted to get a-head in life!

History teacher: How would you discover what life in Ancient Egypt was really like?

Pupil: I'd ask my mummy!

What do toucans sing at Christmas?

Jungle Bells.

How do we know that the ancient Romans had an expensive education?

Because they could all speak Latin.

One boy says to another boy, My pet's called Tiny. "Why?" asks his friend.

Because he's my newt.

Knock, knock!

Who's there?

Alf.

Alf who?

Alf feed the cat while you're abroad!

HA! HA
HA HA!
HA HA HA HA
! HA HA!
HA!

Why couldn't the mummy answer the phone?

He was too wrapped up!

Why did the leopard refuse to take a bath?

Because he didn't want to become spotless.

Why wasn't the werewolf astronaut allowed to land his spaceship?

Because the moon was full!

Why does your teacher have her hair in a bun?

Because she has a face like a burger!

What do you get if you cross a donkey and Christmas?

Muletide greetings!

Who would referee a tennis match between Julius Caesar and Brutus?

A Roman umpire.

Parent: Do you think my son will make a good Arctic explorer?

Teacher: I would think so: most of his grades are below zero!

Why did Dracula advertise for a housekeeper?

He wanted some new blood in the house!

How did the monkey get down the stairs?

It slid down the banana-ster.

HA HA HA

What do cats drink in the desert?

Evaporated milk.

What do you call a dog with a bunch of roses?

A collie-flower!

Why did the farmer's dog keep chasing his tail?

He was trying to make ends meet.

What did the snake give his date when he dropped her off?

A goodnight hiss.

What do you call a woman with a cat on her head?

Kitty.

Why do kindergarten teachers have such a positive attitude?

They know how to make the little things count.

Who do vampires invite to their birthday parties?

Anybody they can dig up!

Who sailed on the ghost ship?

The skeleton crew.

Teacher: Can you tell me what water is?

Pupil: It's a clear liquid that turns black when I put my hands in it!

Who is the world's scariest superhero?

Vampire bat-man!

Did prehistoric people hunt bear?

No, they wore clothes!

What did the dog say when his owner stopped him from chewing the newspaper?

You took the words out of my mouth!

How does a sheep finish a letter?

Sincerely ewes.

What language do oranges speak?

Mandarin.

Why did the mammoth have a furry coat?

Because it would have looked silly in a parka.

What do you get if you drop birdseed in your shoes?

Pigeon toes.

Why should you never tell a giraffe a secret?

Because you could fall off his neck as you whisper in his ear.

Why did the chicken cross the playground?

To get to the other slide!

Why is that boy locked up in a cage in the corner of the classroom?

Oh, he's the teacher's pet!

What do you call a lazy skeleton?

Bone idle!

What sort of telescope lets you see ghosts?

A horrorscope!

What snack did the caveman like best?

A club sandwich.

I think our school must be haunted.

Why?

HA!

Because the teacher keeps talking about the school spirit!

What sort of jokes do chickens like best?

Corny ones!

What did Tarzan tell his son?

Be careful, it's a jungle out there.

Why did the man send his alphabet soup back?

Because he couldn't find words to describe it!

Is chicken soup good for your health?

Not if you're the chicken!

Teacher: Who discovered Pluto?

Pupil: Walt Disney!

What did the clean dog say to the dirty dog?

Long time no flea!

What's sweet and crunchy and swings through the trees?

A meringue-utan.

What did Frankenstein do when the monster's head kept falling off?

He made a bolt for it!

What did Caesar say to Cleopatra?

Toga-ether we can rule the world!

What grows down as it grows up?

A goose!

What ice-cream does a gorilla like best?

Chocolate chimp.

Where do werewolves live?

In warehouses.

What do you call a cat with eight legs?

An octopus.

Teacher: If you multiply 245 by 3,456 and divide the answer by 165, then subtract 752, what will you get?

Pupil: The wrong answer!

Which king had the largest crown?

The one with the biggest head!

Teacher: What came after the Stone Age and the Bronze Age?

Pupil: The sausage?

My dog is a real problem. He chases anything and everything on a bike. I don't know what to do. Just take his bike away!

Teacher: Michael, how do we know that the Earth is round?

Michael: I didn't say it was, Mr. Johnson!

Why is that farmer setting fire to the plants in his field?

He's growing baked beans!

What's worse than a crocodile with a toothache?

A centipede with athlete's foot.

Why do monsters like to stand in a ring?

They love being part of a vicious circle!

Why do giraffes have small appetites?

Because a little goes a long way.

In which era did people sunbathe the most?

The Bronzed Age.

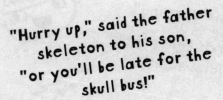

"Hurry up," said the father skeleton to his son, "or you'll be late for the skull bus!"

Teacher: Mary, how did you find the questions in your English test?

Mary: Oh, I found the questions easily enough, it's the answers I couldn't find!

What do you call a man who keeps rabbits?

Warren!

Which cats are great at bowling?

Alley cats.

What sort of dog is good at looking after children?

A baby setter.

What did the ancient Egyptians call bad leaders?

Un-Pharaohs.

HA!

Where do vampire schoolchildren go for field trips?

Lake Eerie!

What do you get if you cross a cow and a jogging machine?

A milk shake!

Why doesn't Dracula have any friends?

Because he's a pain in the neck!

What is hairy and orange and always comes back to you?

A boomerang-utan.

What says, "Moo, baa, woof, quack, meow, oink?"

A sheep that speaks foreign languages!

What happens if you upset a cannibal?

You get into hot water.

LOL

What does Dracula drink?

De-coffin-ated coffee!

Teacher: Please don't talk while you are doing your exam.

Pupil: It's all right, Miss Brown. We're not doing the exam, just talking!

HA HA HA

Doctor, I think I'm a cat!

How long have you felt like this?

Since I was a kitten!

What happened to the knight who lost his left arm and left leg in battle?

He was all right in the end.

Teacher: How good are you at picking up music?

Pupil: Well, I'm not sure if I could lift a whole piano!

Where do Egyptian mummies go for a swim?

To the Dead Sea.

What do you get if a cat sits on a beach at Christmas?

Sandy claws!

What do you get if you cross a gorilla with a porcupine?

A seat on the bus!

What is the best time to pick apples?

When the farmer is away!

What do you get if you cross a cow with a camel?

Lumpy milkshakes!

First cat: Where do fleas go in the winter?

Second cat: Search me!

Teacher: Why were you late this morning, Veronica?

Veronica: I squeezed the toothpaste too hard, and it took me half an hour to get it all back into the tube again!

How did Columbus's men sleep on the boat?

With their eyes shut.

Where do sheep
get shorn?

At the baa-baas!

**What do you
call a kind,
helpful monster
who likes flowers
and butterflies?**

A failure!

**What do you give a gorilla
that's going to throw up?**

Plenty of room!

What did the old vampire say when he broke his teeth?

Fangs for the memory...

What has lots of ears, but can't hear anything at all?

A cornfield.

Which animals were the last to leave Noah's Ark?

The elephants; they had to pack their trunks.

How does a teacher remove hard wax from his ears?

He works it out with a pencil!

What happened to the Scottish cat who ran into the road without looking?

It was kilt!

What do you call a blind dinosaur?

Doyouthinkhesaurus.

HA!

Pupil: Can we do some work on the Iron Age today?

Teacher: Well, I'm not certain, I'm a bit rusty on that period of history!

Why did Eve move to New York?

She fell for the Big Apple.

How do you find a lost dog?

Make a sound like a bone!

**What does it say
on the mummy's
garage entrance?**

Toot, and come in!

HA! HA
HA HA HA!
HA HA HA HA!
! HA ! HA!
HA!

**What happens if you
cross an elephant
and a canary?**

A very messy cage.

How does your dog get
into the house?

Through the labra-door!

HA HA HA

What has two
eyes, two legs and
two noses?

Two pirates!

Why are you
throwing garlic out
of the window?

To keep vampires away.

But there aren't any
vampires here.

See, it works!

LOL

What's the most
dangerous animal
in your backyard?

The clothes-lion.

Teacher: Can you define dogmatic?

Pupil: Is it a robot pet?

Teacher: What was Robin Hood's mum called?

Pupil: Mother Hood.

What does it mean if you find a set of horse shoes?

A horse is walking around in his socks!

Why did the boy stand behind the horse?

He thought he might get a kick out of it.

Did you hear about the cat who sucked a lemon?

He was a sourpuss.

What class do snakes like best at school?

Hisssstory.

Ten cats were at the movies. One walked out. How many were left?

None, they were all copycats!

> Where did the pilgrims land when they came to America?
>
> On their feet!

Why did the giant robot feel sick after eating a train?

He caught a commuter virus!

Who was the winner of the headless horse race?

No one. They all finished neck and neck!

What did the executioner say to the former king?

It's time to head off!

Mother: Time to get up and go to school!

Son: I don't want to go! Everyone hates me and I get bullied!

Mother: But you have to go, you're the principal!

What do you call an exploding ape?

A ba-BOOM!

What do you get from a forgetful cow?

Milk of amnesia.

What sport do horses like best?

Stable tennis.

What's the difference between a well-dressed gentleman and an exhausted dog?

One wears an expensive suit and the other just pants.

What do you get if you cross a snake with a pig?

A boar constrictor.

What did the alien say to the plant?

Take me to your weeder!

What do you call a pyramid overlooking the Nile?

A tomb with a view.

If having hairy palms is the first sign of turning into a monster, what is the second?

Looking for them!

Teacher: Did you know that most accidents happen in the kitchen?

Pupil: Yes, but we still have to eat them!

What did the cowboy say when he saw a cow in a tree?

Howdy get there?

What did you learn in school today?

Not enough. I have to go back tomorrow!

What do ghosts do if they are afraid?

Hide under a sheet!

If you had fifteen cows and five goats, what would you have?

Plenty of milk!

Doctor, I feel as sick as a dog.

I'll make an appointment for you to see a vet!

What did the banana say to the gorilla?

Nothing, bananas can't talk!

Teacher: How many seconds are there in a year?

Pupil: Twelve: January 2nd, February 2nd...

Patient: Doctor, I feel like a goat!

Doctor: Really? And how are the kids?

Mother: Did you put the cat out?

Kid: I didn't need to. It wasn't on fire!

Why did Godzilla stop eating buildings?

He got atomic ache!

HA HA HA

Which Egyptian pharaoh played the trumpet?

Tootin' Kamun.

What do you get when you cross an elephant with a kangaroo?

Big holes all over Australia.

What do history teachers talk about when they get together?

The good old days.

Why did the monster have twins in his lunchbox?

In case he felt like seconds!

Why do elephants never forget?

Because no one ever tells them anything.

What do you use to clean a cat's hair?

A catacomb.

Why did the lamb call the police?

It had been fleeced!

I banged my head on the locker door this morning!

Have you seen the school nurse?

No, just stars!

What do you get from a pampered cow?

Milk that's spoiled.

What do you give a sick parakeet?

Tweetment!

What did the music teacher need a ladder for?

Reaching the high notes!

Why didn't the vampire laugh at the joke about the wooden stake?

He didn't get the point!

Why did the leopard eat the tightrope walker?

He wanted a balanced diet.

What do you call a prehistoric monster when it is asleep?

A dino-snore.

Teacher: Why is your homework late, young man?

Pupil: Sorry, Miss Elliot, my dad is a slow writer!

Why did the werewolf swallow a bag full of coins?

Because he thought the change would do him good!

Why did Columbus cross the ocean?

To get to the other tide.

What do you call a pig with three eyes?

A piiig.

What's the difference between a fish and a piano?

You can't tuna fish!

What happened when the dog went to the flea circus?

He stole the show!

What did one flea say to the other flea?

Should we walk or take the dog?

Why do insects hum?

Because they can never remember the words!

Did you hear about the kid who had his ID stolen?

Now he's just a k.

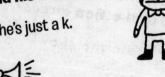

Why did the chicken run out on to the basketball court?

Because the referee whistled for a fowl!

Did you hear about the woman who went in for plastic surgery, and came out looking like a Martian?

She told the surgeon she wanted to look like a million dollars, so he made her face all green and crinkly!

What do you get if you cross a skeleton and a dog?

An animal that buries itself!

What's the best way to catch a fish?

Get someone to throw it at you.

What is the first thing a monster eats when he goes to a restaurant?

The waiter!

HA HA HA

Who's that at the door?

The invisible man.

Tell him I can't see him.

Spotted in the library:

Robots Are People Too by Anne Droid.

Why did the cookie cry?

Because his mother had been a wafer so long.

What did the polite sheep say to his friend at the gate?

After ewe.

What do you call a fairy that has never taken a bath?

Stinkerbell

What happened to the robot who put his shoes on the wrong feet?

He had to be rebooted.

When do truck drivers stop for a snack?

When they see a fork in the road.

**What's black and
white and red all
over?**

A sunburned penguin!

Why do zombies always look
so tired?

They are dead on their feet!

**What do cows eat
for breakfast?**

Moosli!

Which weighs the most, a full moon or a half moon?

A half moon, because a full moon is much lighter!

What do you get if you cross a crocodile with a camera?

A snapshot!

Young man, can you reach that package of beef from the top of the freezer?

No ma'am. The steaks are too high.

Waiter, this food tastes funny.

Then why aren't you laughing?

What's orange and points North?

A magnetic carrot.

Why is Frankenstein's monster bad at school?

He doesn't have the brains he was born with!

First robot: Are you enjoying that book about magnetism?

Second robot: Yes, I can't put it down!

Why did the rhubarb go out with a prune?

Because he couldn't find a date.

What do witches sing at Christmas?

Deck the Halls with Poison Ivy.

A police officer saw a man walking down the street with a penguin. He told the man to take the penguin to the zoo. Good idea, the man said, and off he went. The next day, the police officer saw the man again. He still had the penguin with him.

I told you to take that penguin to the zoo, the police officer said.

I did, the man replied. He really enjoyed that, so today I'm taking him to the movies.

Knock knock.

Who's there?

Jupiter.

Jupiter who?

Jupiter spaceship on my lawn?

How do you get a baby astronaut to sleep?

Rocket.

How can you tell two octopuses are dating?

Because they walk along arm in arm in arm in arm in arm in arm in arm in arm!

Why wasn't the girl scared when a shark swam past her?

She'd been told it was a man-eater.

**What did the
headless ghost
get when he fell
through a window?**

A pane in the neck!

Why was the
thirsty astronaut
hanging out near
the computer
keyboard?

He was looking for
the space bar.

**This coffee
is disgusting,
it tastes like
mud.**

I'm not surprised,
it was ground a
few minutes ago!

Why did the chef serve frozen steak?

He wanted it to melt in the mouth.

Baby ogre: When I grow up, I want to drive a tank!

Mother ogre: Well, I certainly won't stand in your way!

Why did the Apple Mac programmer live in the dark?

Because he refused to use Windows.

First leopard: Hey, is that a jogger over there?

Second leopard: Yes, great, I love fast food!

HA
HA
HA

How could you give yourself an injury gathering shellfish?

You might pull a mussel.

Teacher: William, how fast does light travel?

William: I don't know, it's already arrived by the time I wake up!

What's an elephant's fave game?

Squash.

Which is the most stylish planet?

Saturn. It has a lot of rings.

How do fish go into business?

They start on a small scale.

What do you get if you cross a comedian and an orange?

Peels of laughter.

Did you hear about the couple who adopted a calculator?

It made a great addition to the family.

What do monster children do on Halloween?

They go from door to door dressed as humans!

Why did the boy bring a surfboard to school?

The teacher said they were going to be surfing the Internet.

How many guests has the zombie invited to his party

It depends on who he could dig up!

What do you call an airplane passenger covered in salt and pepper?

A seasoned sightseer.

When can you be sure that the moon won't eat you?

When it's a full moon.

What day do fish hate?

Fry day.

What do you get if you cross a snake with a bird?

A feather boa constrictor!

Why was the computer such a terrific golfer?

It had a hard drive.

What has four legs, big ears, and a trunk?

A mouse going on vacation.

What crazy bug lives on the moon?

The lunar tick.

What did the speedy tomato say to the slow tomato?

Ketchup!

Where do ocean scientists keep their coffee mugs?

On the continental shelf.

Why did the pixie move out of the toadstool?

Because there wasn't mushroom.

Spotted in the library:

I Fell Down a Rabbit Hole by Alison Wonderland.

What happened at the cannibals' wedding?

They toasted the bride and groom.

What do you call a man with a cable coming out of his ear?

Mike!

Where do fish keep their savings?

In the river bank!

What do ghostly police officers do?

They haunt down criminals!

HA!

An astronaut and a chimp were fired off into space. The chimp opened its sealed orders, read them, and immediately started programming the flight computer. The astronaut opened his sealed orders and found only one instruction:

Feed the chimp!

What happened when the boat carrying red paint crashed into one carrying blue paint?

Both crews were marooned.

How do aliens go fishing?

With Earth-worms!

What's big, red, and eats rocks?

A big, red rock-eater!

How do lumberjacks get on the Internet?

They log on.

What do penguins do in their spare time?

They chill.

HA
HA
HA

Waiter, waiter, there's a button in my lettuce.

Ah! That will be from the salad dressing, sir!

Why did the man eat yeast and furniture polish for breakfast?

He wanted to rise and shine.

What do you buy for someone who already has all the latest gadgets?

A burglar alarm.

What did the short-sighted porcupine say to the cactus?

Ah, there you are, Dad!

What lies at the heart of gravity?

The letter V.

Why don't giants speak to leprechauns?

They're no good at small talk. "

What do you call a man floating up and down on the sea?

Bob.

What do you call a dead skunk?

Ex-stinked!

Why are dolphins smarter than humans?

Because they can train humans to stand by the side of the pool and throw them fish.

Why didn't the astronaut get burned when he landed on the sun?

He went there at night!

Why do robots never feel queasy?

They have cast iron stomachs.

Knock knock.

Who's there?

Arthur.

Arthur who?

Arthur any cookies left?

What do you call two witches who live together?

Broommates!

Why was the mother firefly sad?

Because her children weren't very bright!

Did you hear about the incredibly clever monster?

He was called Frank Einstein.

How do you make a fruit punch?

Give it boxing lessons.

Why did the pupil fall asleep in computer class?

He was feeling key-bored.

Why do little green men have nice, warm homes?

Because they live in little greenhouses!

Who stole the soap from the bathtub?

A robber duckie.

What do you give a robot who feels like a light snack?

Some 60-watt bulbs!

Why are parties on the moon always so dull?

There's no atmosphere.

Why couldn't the wizard move?

He was spellbound!

Why did the girl stare at the orange juice carton?

Because it said concentrate on the label.

What is the traditional anthem of the pig navy?

Oinkers Aweigh.

What is the best thing to do when a hippo sneezes?

Get out of the way!

What kind of fish are useful in cold weather?

Skates.

Why was the chef so relaxed?

He had plenty of thyme on his hands!

BOOM!

HA HA HA

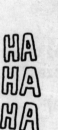

What would you do if a jellyfish stung you?

I'd break every bone in its body!

Why did the robot get angry?

Someone kept pushing his buttons!

What do Italian ghosts eat for dinner?

Spookhetti!

Book spotted in the school library:

Is There Life on Mars? by Howard I. No.

Why do astronomers always bang their heads?

It helps them to see stars!

What did the monster say to the scruffy werewolf?

You look like you're going to the dogs!

What's yellow and dangerous?

Shark-infested custard.

What lives in a forest and tells the dullest stories ever heard?

A wild boar!

Customer: Why is there a dead fly in my soup?

Waiter: Well, you surely don't expect to get a live one at these prices!

What do you get if you cross a large computer and a hamburger?

A Big Mac!

Waiter, waiter, there's a fly in my soup!

Sorry, madam, I didn't know you were vegetarian!

What's the difference between computer hardware and software?

Hardware is the stuff that you can kick when it doesn't work.

What did the silliest kid in school call his pet zebra?

Spot!

Three badly made robots were playing cards.

The first one threw his hand in. The second one rolled his eyes. The third one laughed his head off.

What do sea monsters eat?

Fish and ships!

Why would Snow White be a good judge?

Because she is the fairest in the land.

Where do you normally find elves?

It depends where you left them!

What does a frog use to put up shelves?

A toad's tool!

What's fluffy and green?

A seasick poodle.

What did one rocket say to the other?

I wish I could quit smoking!

Which fairy-tale creature has the most teeth?

A dragon?

No, the tooth fairy!

Did you hear about the turkey who tried to escape the roasting pan?

He was foiled.

Teacher: Give me an example of cutting-edge technology.

Pupil: A pair of scissors?

Why was the skeleton's jacket in shreds?

Because he had very sharp shoulder blades!

What goes in one year and out the other?

A time machine!

What are apricots?

Where baby monkeys sleep!

Why don't astronauts keep their jobs for long?

Because after their training they're always fired.

Why are hyenas always falling out?

They always have a bone to pick with each other!

HA! HA HA HA! HA HA HA HA! HA I HA! HA!

Why did the crab cross the road?

To get to the other tide.

Some meteorites collide with planets. What do you call meteorites that miss?

Meteowrongs.

BOOM!

My computer is powered by clockwork.

Really?

No, I was just winding you up.

How did the fruit bats go into Noah's Ark?

In pears!

How do you know when a cannibal feels like eating you?

He keeps buttering you up!

How do two ghosts decide who owns something?

They fright each other for it!

Where is the safest place to see a man-eating fish?

In a seafood restaurant.

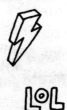

What are the scariest dinosaurs?

Terror dactyls!

What did the fat man say when he sat down at the dinner table?

Just think, all this food is going to waist!

What grades did the pirate get in school?

High seas.

How can you tell if a robot is happy to see you?

Because his eyes light up.

What did the No Parking sign outside the witch's house say?

Violators will be toads!

What did one asteroid say to the other asteroid?

Pleased to meteor."

Why did the alien turn the restaurant staff upside down?

Someone told him that you had to tip the waiter!

Why did the headless ghost go to the psychiatrist?

Because he wasn't all there!

What music do robots like to listen to?

Heavy metal!

Which salad ingredient is the most dangerous for ocean liners?

Iceberg lettuce.

What sort of fish would you find in a bird cage?

A perch!

How do you make golden soup?

Put 14 carrots in it!

What do you get if you divide the circumference of a pumpkin by its diameter?

Pumpkin pi.

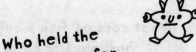

Who held the baby octopus for ransom?

Squidnappers!

What do you call a criminal bird?

An illegal eagle!

What type of spells did the whirling wizard cast?

Dizzy spells.

What do aliens
cook their
breakfasts on?

Unidentified frying
objects.

What do you get from robot sheep?

Steel wool.

What sort of horses do monsters ride?

Night mares!

Why was the electrified robot so badly behaved?

It didn't know how to conduct itself.

HA!

How does the solar system hold up its clothes?

With an asteroid belt.

What's the best medicine for seasickness?

Vitamin sea.

A pizza walks into a bar and asks for a burger.

I'm sorry, says the barman. We don't serve food.

What noise does a witch's car make?

Broom, broom!

What do you get if you cross a bad golfer and an outboard motor?

I'm not sure, but I bet it goes, Putt, putt, putt, putt.

What goes cackle, squelch, cackle, squelch?

A witch in soggy tennis shoes.

Chef: I didn't use a recipe for this casserole, I made it up out of my own head!

Customer: I thought it tasted of sawdust!

**Why did the
computer
programmer give
up his job?**

He lost his drive.

**What do young
astronauts sit on
during takeoff?**

Booster seats.

**How do you catch a
squirrel?**

Climb a tree and act like
a nut.

Did you hear about the robot dog?

His megabark was worse than his megabyte.

Why was the zebra put in charge of the jungle army?

Because he had the most stripes!

What type of snack does an alien love best?

A Martian-mallow.

If I cut a potato in two, I have two halves

If I cut a potato in four, I have four quarters.

What do I have if I cut a potato in 16?

French fries!

What do you call a magician's assistant?

Magic Trixie!

Which fish come out at night?

Starfish.

What's big, furry, and flies?

A hot-air baboon.

Why did the bakers work late?

Because they kneaded the dough!

Who wins all the money at the undersea poker games?

Card sharks.

Why didn't the witch sing a solo at the concert?

Because she had a frog in her throat.

What do you call a robot who turns into a tractor?

A trans-farmer!

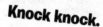

Knock knock.

Who's there?

Phil.

Phil who?

Phil this cup with sugar, would you, I've run out!

Why did the alien build a spaceship from feathers?

He wanted to travel light years!

Where do cool mice live?

In mouse pads.

What do you call a vampire that hides in the kitchen?

Spatula!

How do you stop moles from digging up your lawn?

Hide the shovels.

What happens if you cross an electric eel with a sponge?

You get a shock absorber.

How much did the pirate pay for his corn?

A buck an ear.

Waiter, can I have my lunch on the patio?

Certainly, sir, but most people find a plate more sensible!

Why do pirates have a hard time learning the alphabet?

Because they spend so long at C.

What's the difference between a crazy rabbit and a counterfeit bank note?

One's a mad bunny and the other's bad money.

Why was the ogre catching centipedes?

He wanted scrambled legs for breakfast!

What did the boy star say to the girl star?

Do you want to glow out with me?

Did you know that my computer can do the gardening?

Can it really?

Yes, it's made with cutting-hedge technology.

What sea creatures do you find on legal documents?

Seals.

Why do astronauts have to prepare a meal before blastoff?

They get hungry at launch time.

Which city has no people?

Electricity.

Why do whales sing?

Because they can't talk!

Why should you never tell secrets in a corn field?

Because you would be surrounded by ears!

What did the police do to the giant who ran away with the circus?

They made him bring it back.

HA HA HA

How do you close an envelope underwater?

With a seal.

Where would you find a suitable gift for a tortured ghost?

In a chain store!

What farm animal can you spread on toast?

A baby goat, it's a little butter!

Why should you never trust a whale with your deepest, darkest secrets?

Because they're all blubbermouths.

Why was the thirsty astronaut loitering near the computer keyboard?

He was looking for the space bar.

Did you hear about the two TVs who got married?

Their reception was excellent.

What runs and runs without ever getting out of breath?

A river.

Where do camels keep their money?

In sand banks.

Why do astronauts make good American football players?

They know how to make a great touchdown!

What's the most expensive item on the menu at a Chinese restaurant?

Fortune cookies.

Which great detective is three feet tall and has pointed ears?

Sherlock Gnomes.

Why did the robot kiss his girlfriend?

He just couldn't resistor.

What do the underwater police travel in?

Squid cars!

Mmmmm! This cake is lovely and warm!

It should be; the cat's been sitting on it all afternoon!

What happened to the boxer who got knocked out by Dracula?

He was out for the Count.

Where do tadpoles change into frogs?

In a croakroom.

How did the inventor of the jetpack feel?

He was on cloud nine!

Big alien: If this planet is Mars, what's that one over there?

Little alien: Is it Pa's?

What sort of snacks can you buy on a Chinese boat?

Junk food!

What do rhinoceroses have that no other animal has?

Baby rhinoceroses.

What do computer operators eat for a snack?

Chips!

How do they eat their chips?

One byte at a time.

What did one snowman say to the other snowman?

Smells like carrots.

HA!

Did you hear about the vampire who fell asleep in the wrong coffin?

It was a grave mistake! "

Why did the boy and girl robots call things off after their first date?

There was no spark.

Which snack is wicked and lives in the desert?

The sand witch!

Why did the storekeeper refuse to serve italic fonts?

He didn't like their type.

Knock, knock.

Who's there?

Aladdin.

Aladdin who?

Aladdin the street who wants to come in!

How did Robinson Crusoe survive after his ship sank?

He found some soap and washed himself ashore.

What holds the moon up?

Moon beams.

What sort of animal will never oversleep?

A llama clock!

Why wouldn't the sailor eat any fruitcake?

He was worried about dangerous currants.

Why can't leopards hide from hunters?

Because they are always spotted!

Did you know that they have found life on another planet?

Really?

Yes, there are fleas on Pluto!

Where did the tightrope walker meet his girlfriend?

Online.

How do you keep flies out of your kitchen?

Move the pile of rotting vegetables into the living room!

Why can't you borrow money from a leprechaun?

Because he's always a little short.

How do snowmen get online?

They use the Winternet.

What is the difference between a dragon and a mouse?

Have you had your eyes tested recently?

What starts and ends with t, and is also full of t?

A teapot.

Why did the Sun go to school?

To get brighter.

What do you get if you cross an angry sheep with a mad cow?

An animal that's in a baaaaaaaaaaaaaaaad mooooooooooooood.

What sort of boats do clever schoolchildren travel on?

Scholar-ships!

What kind of bird is at every meal?

A swallow.

How does a tiny robot say goodbye?

With a micro-wave.

When do kangaroos propose marriage?

In leap years!

Who lights up a haunted house?

The lights witch.

Why do the French like eating snails?

Because they don't like fast food!

Which vegetables do pirates like best?

Aaaaartichokes.

Where do rabbits learn to fly?

In the Hare Force!

Why did the vampire always carry a bottle of tomato ketchup?

He was a vegetarian!

Why did the witch buy a computer?

She needed a spell-checker!

Did you hear about the tiny, winged Egyptian king?

He was a fairy pharaoh!

Why are grandma's teeth like stars?

Because they come out at night.

HA!

What did the deep-sea diver yell when he got caught in seaweed?

Kelp!

What do you get if you meet a shark in the Arctic Ocean?

Frostbite.

What did the big candle say to the little candle?

I'm going out tonight.

Where do you leave your spaceship when you visit another planet?

At a parking meteor!

Did you hear about the spiders who got married?

They had a huge webbing.

Brad: Have you seen my high-tech watch belt?

Suzie: It sounds like a waist of time.

What is the one thing that stays hot in the refrigerator?

Mustard!

What did the chewing gum say to the shoe?

I'm stuck on you.

What was the first animal in space?

The cow that jumped over the moon.

What job did the spider get?

Web designer!

Why did the head druid keep falling over?

He couldn't get the staff.

Why do cats hate flying saucers?

Because they can't reach the milk!

How many ears does a robot have?

Three: A left ear, a right ear, and just in case they go wrong, an engine-ear.

What do you call a worm in a fur coat?

A caterpillar!

Why did the tomato blush?

Because he saw the salad dressing.

How do you fix a jack-o'-lantern?

Use a pumpkin patch